Schott New York

T0103098

Spears
b.1977

Toccata (Wild Horses)

for solo piano

Full score

ED 30286

Mainz · London · Madrid · New York · Paris · Prague · Tokyo · Toronto
© 2012 Schott Helicon Music Corporation, New York · Printed in USA

Commissioned by Marika Bournaki

Duration

ca. 5 minutes

World Premiere

October 9, 2012; Montreal, Canada
Place des Arts: Theatre Maisonneuve
Marika Bournaki, piano

Piano

TOCCATA

"WILD HORSES"

for Marika Bournaki

Gregory Spears (2012)

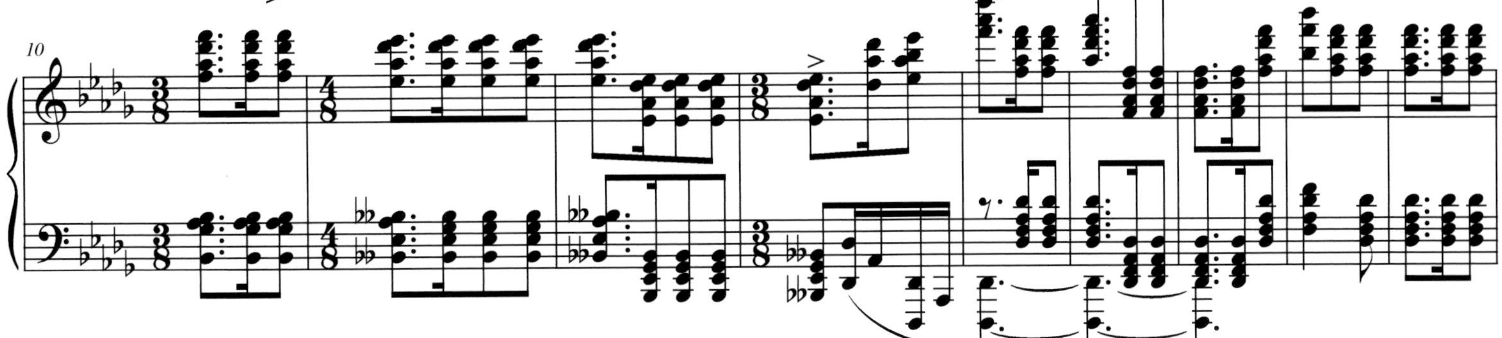

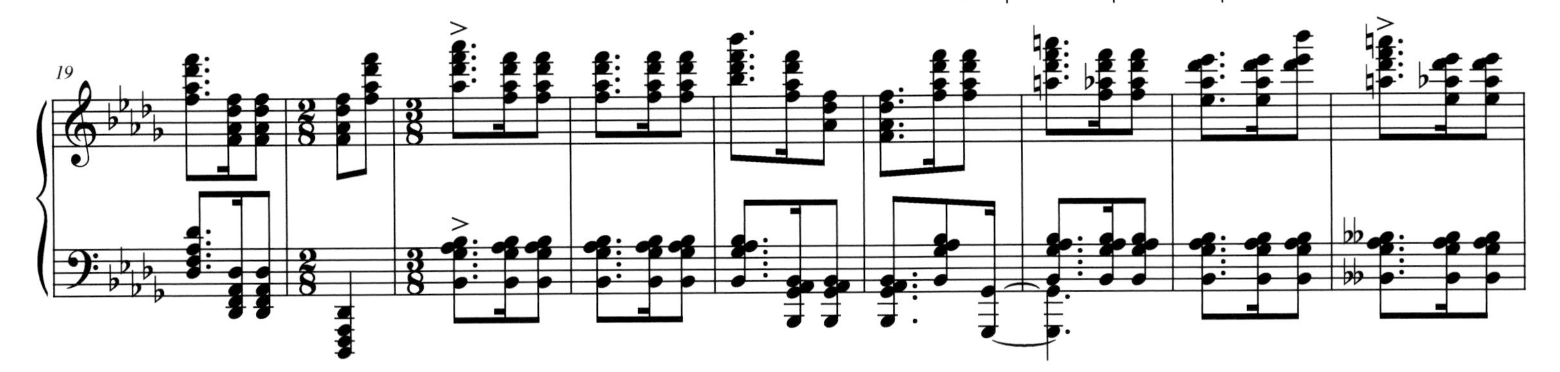

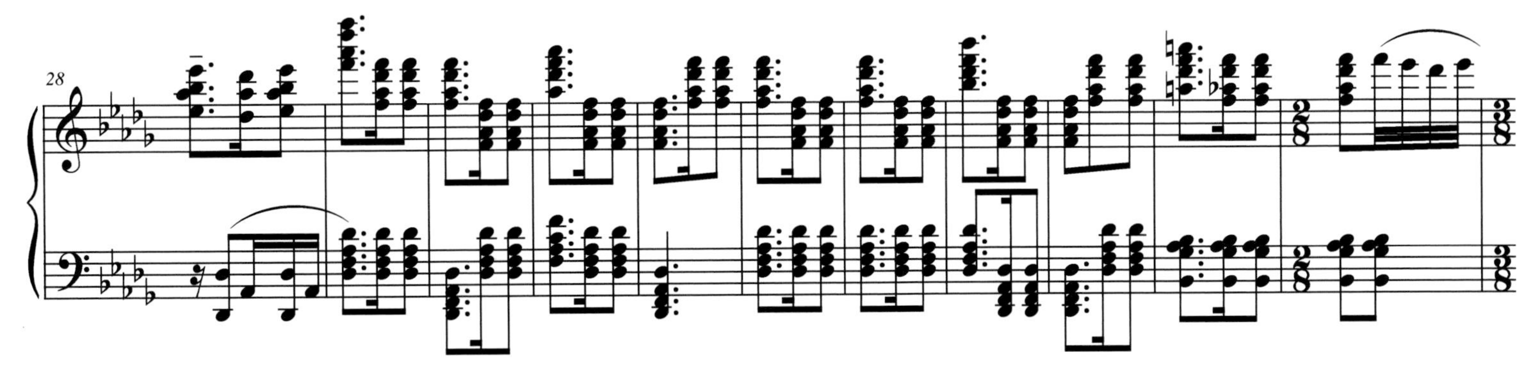

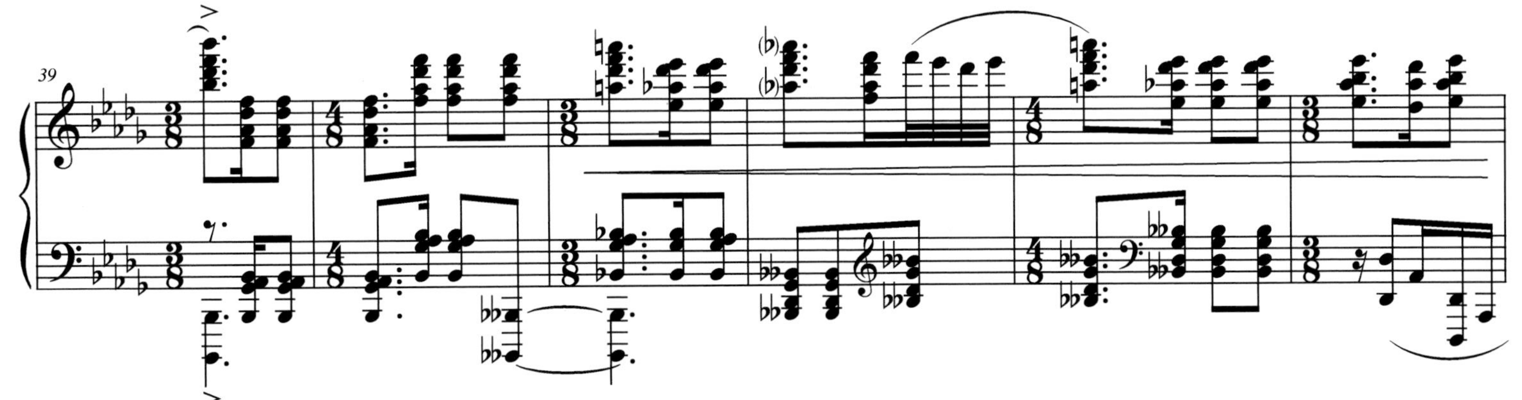

© 2012 Schott Helicon Music Corporation, New York (BMI)

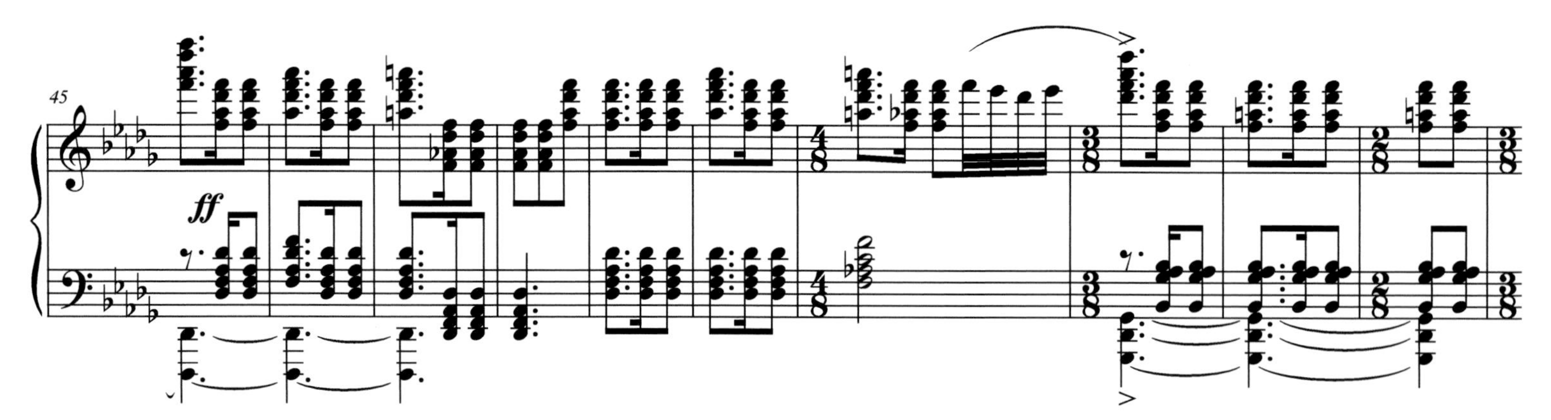
45
ff

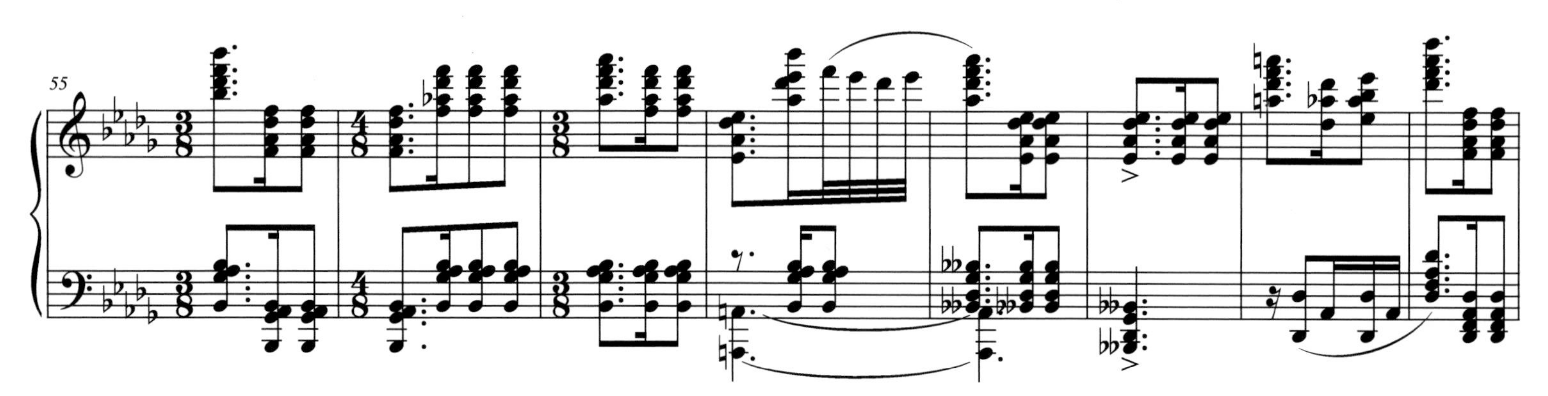
55

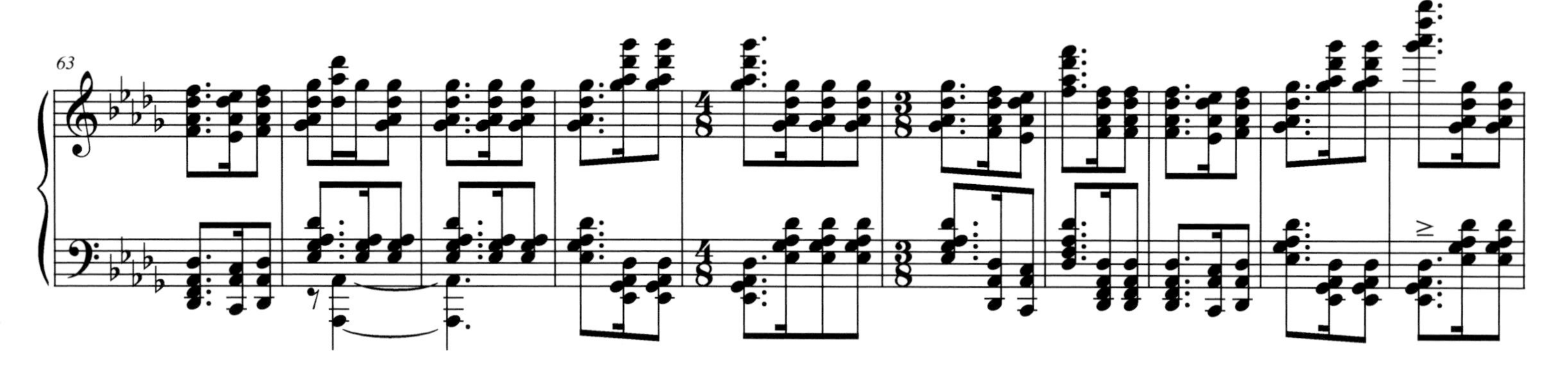
63

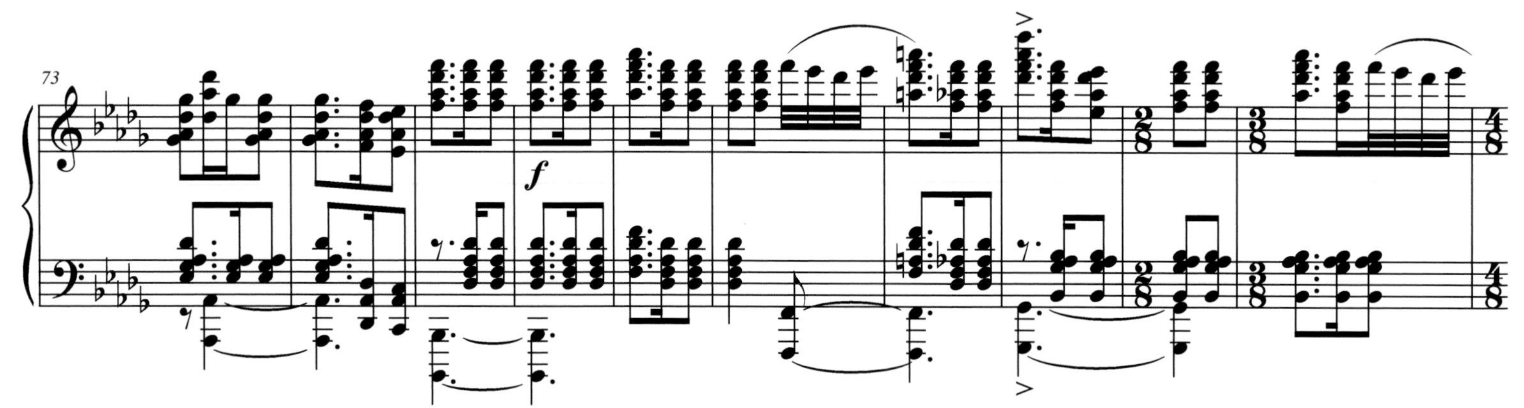
73
f

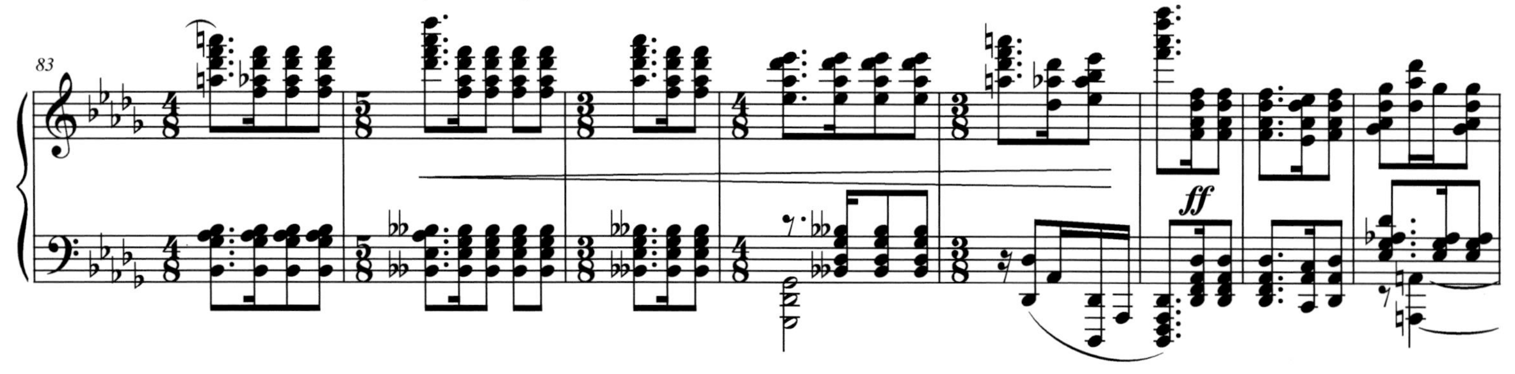
83
ff

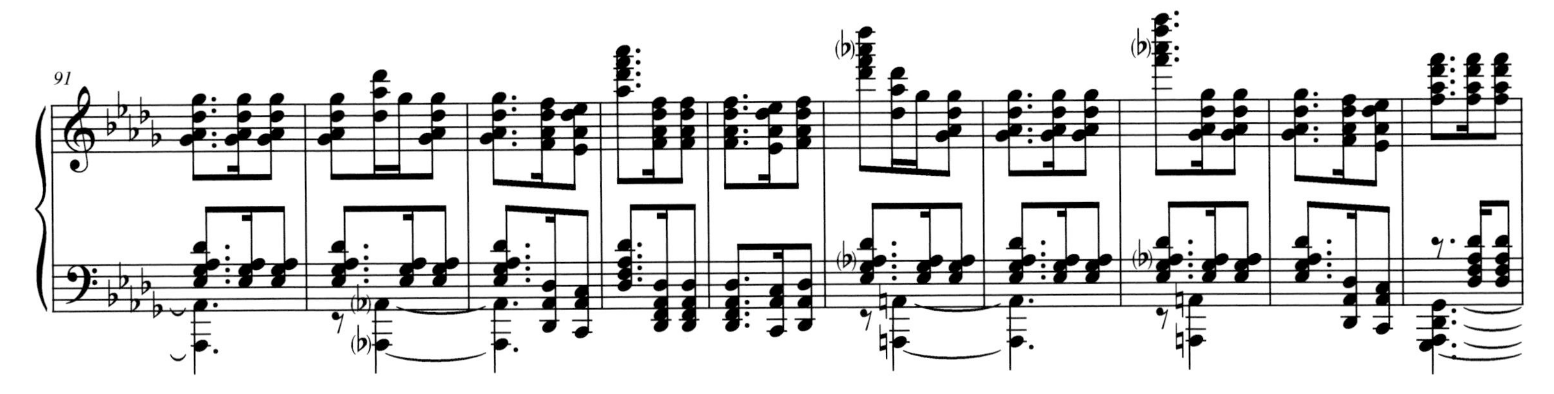

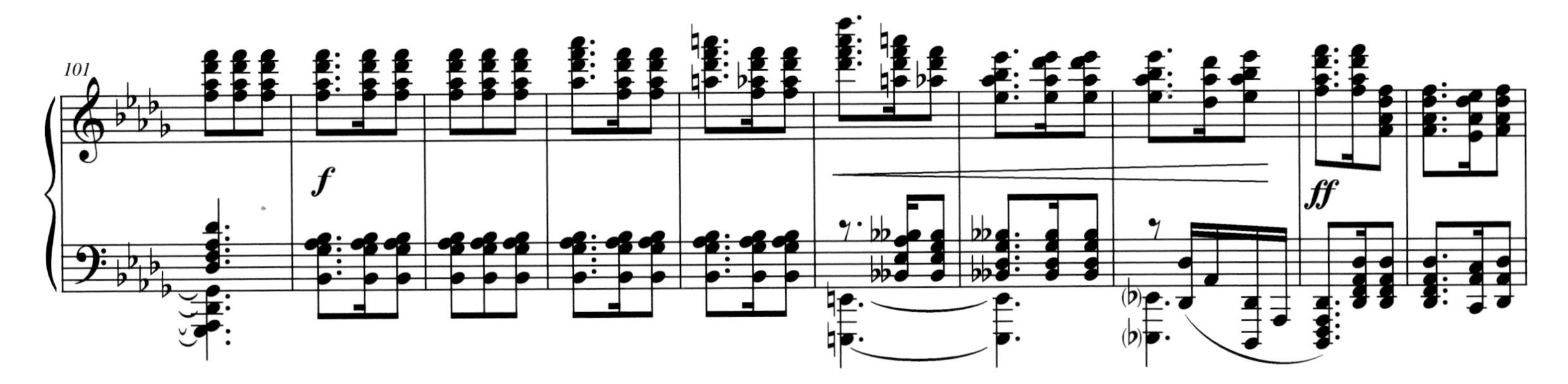

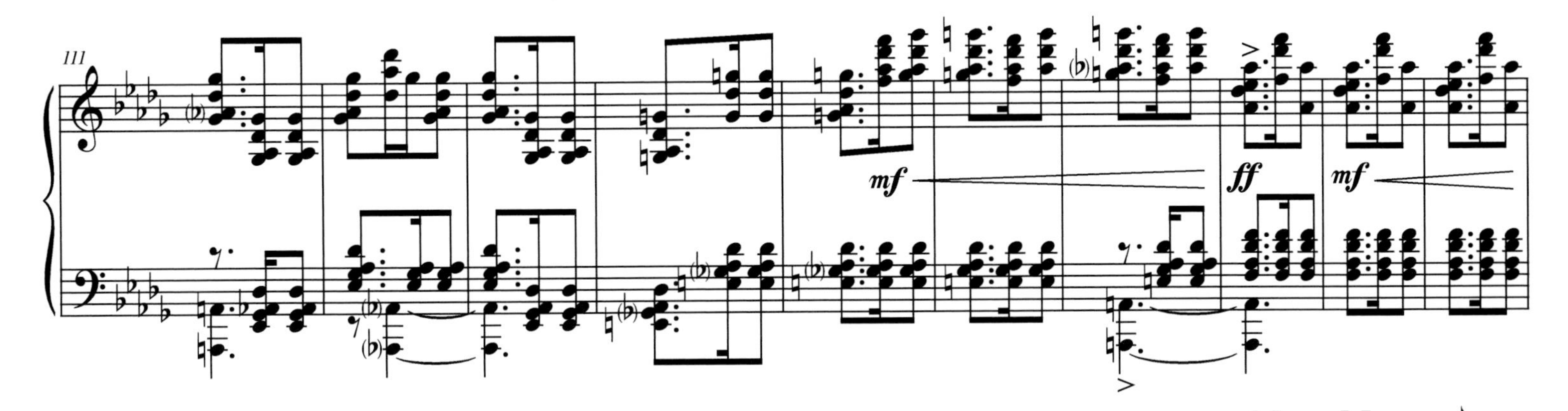

Meno Mosso ♪= 152

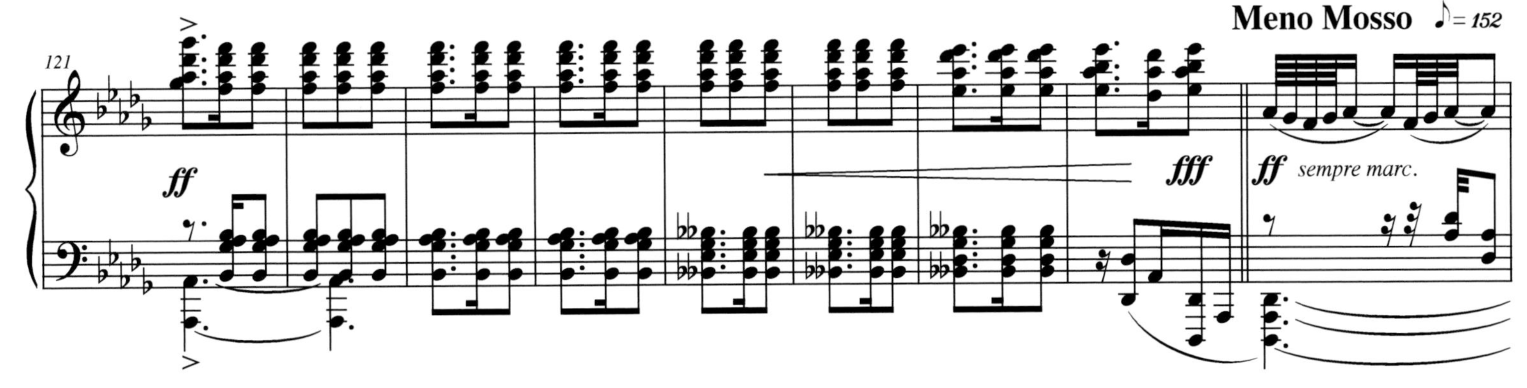

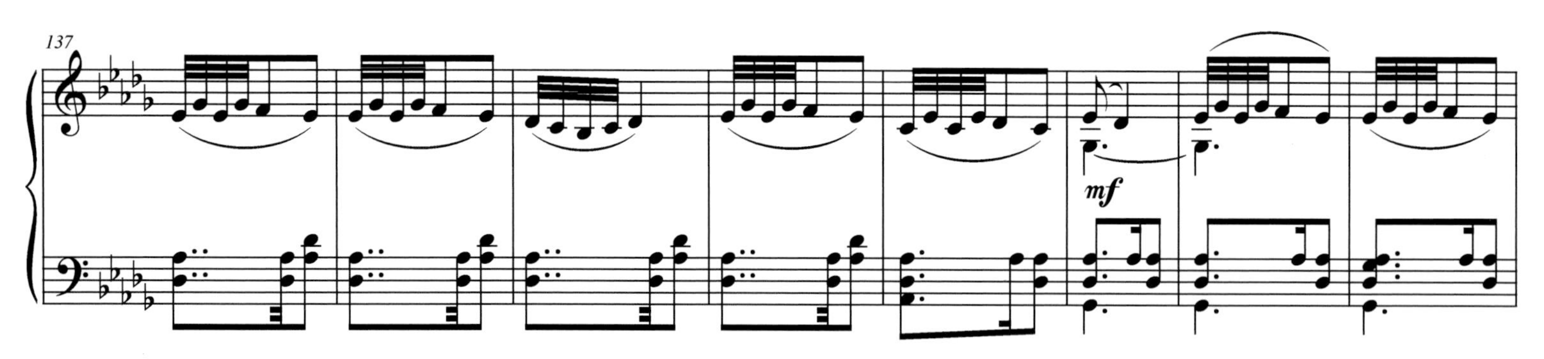
137
mf

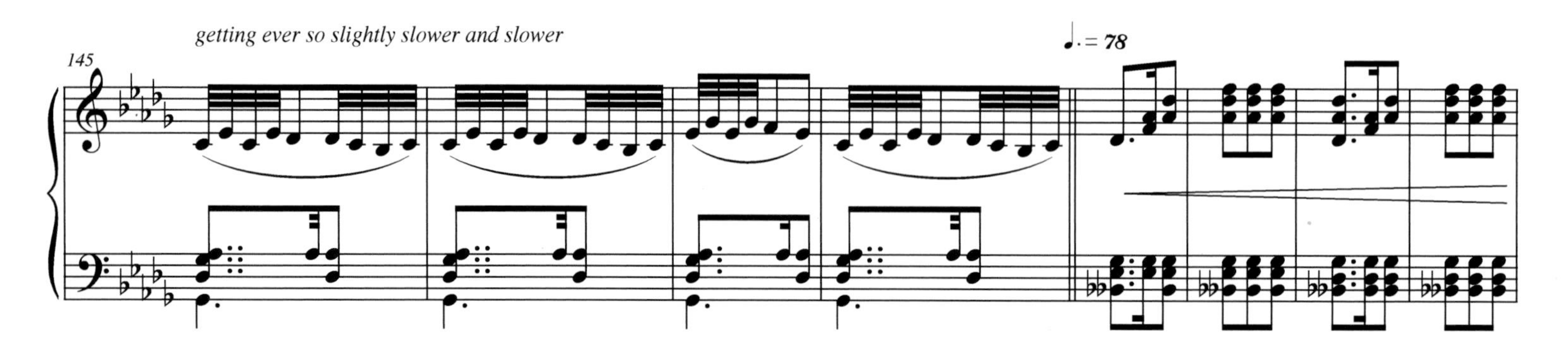
getting ever so slightly slower and slower
145
♩. = 78

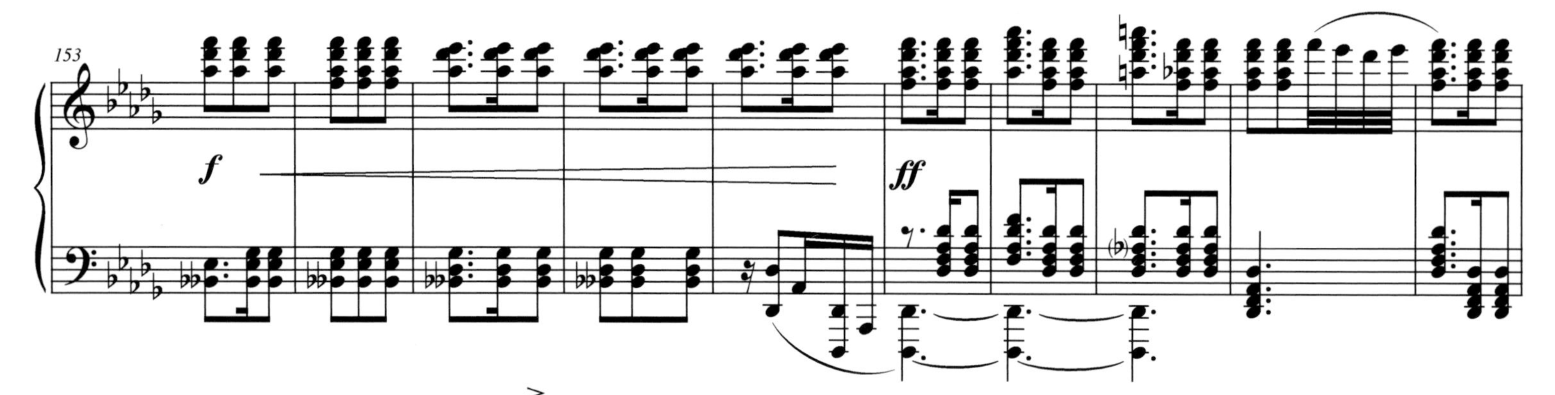
153
f
ff

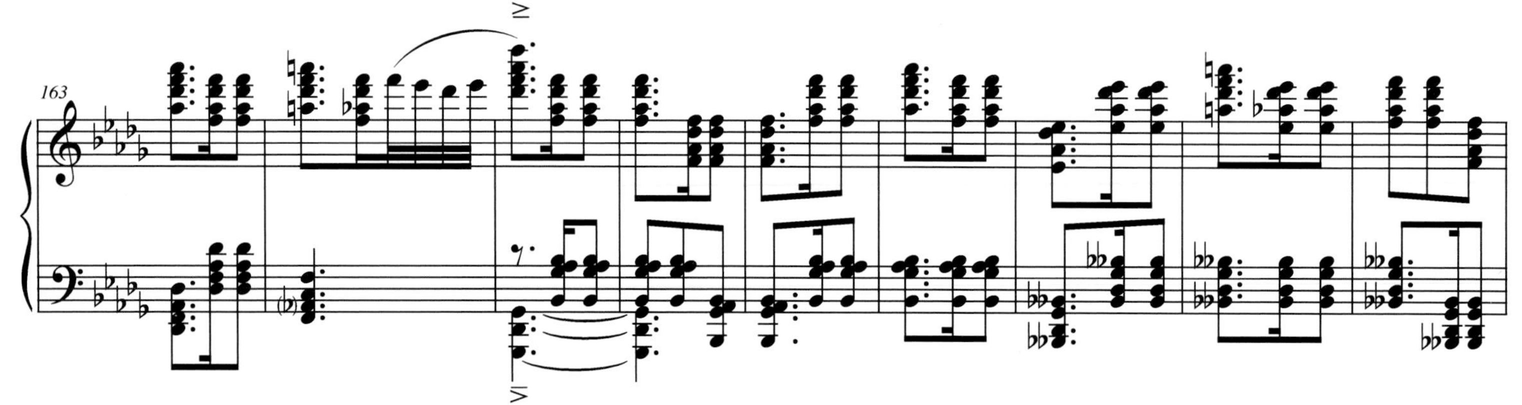
163

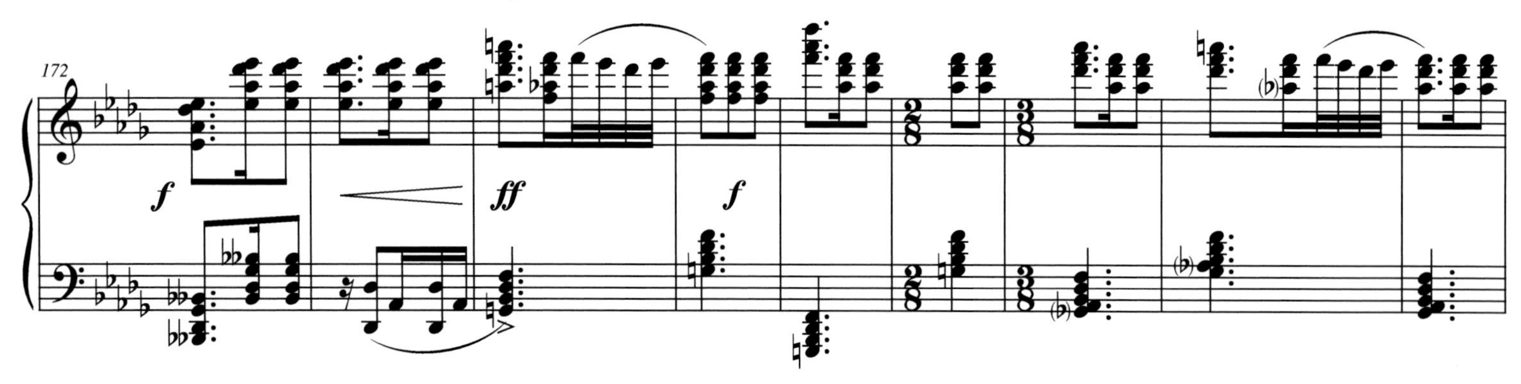
172
f
ff
f

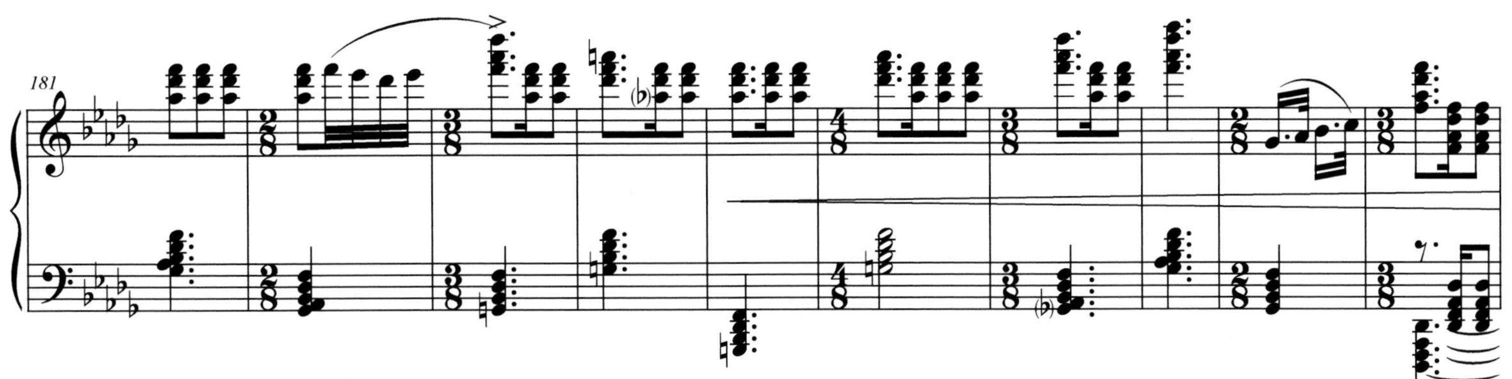
181

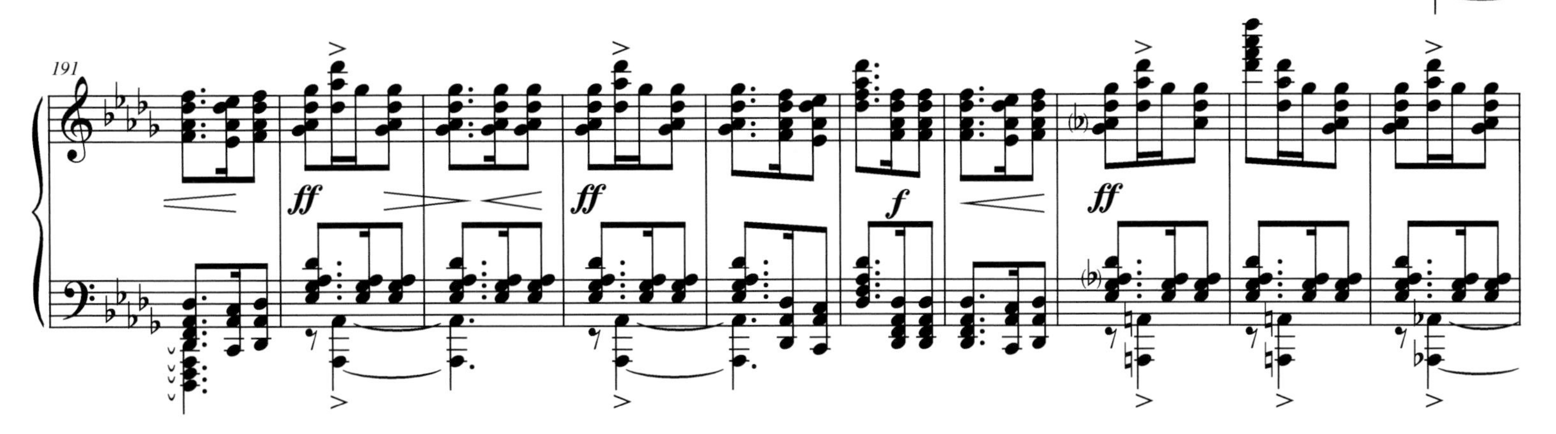
191
ff
ff
f
ff

201
mf
ff

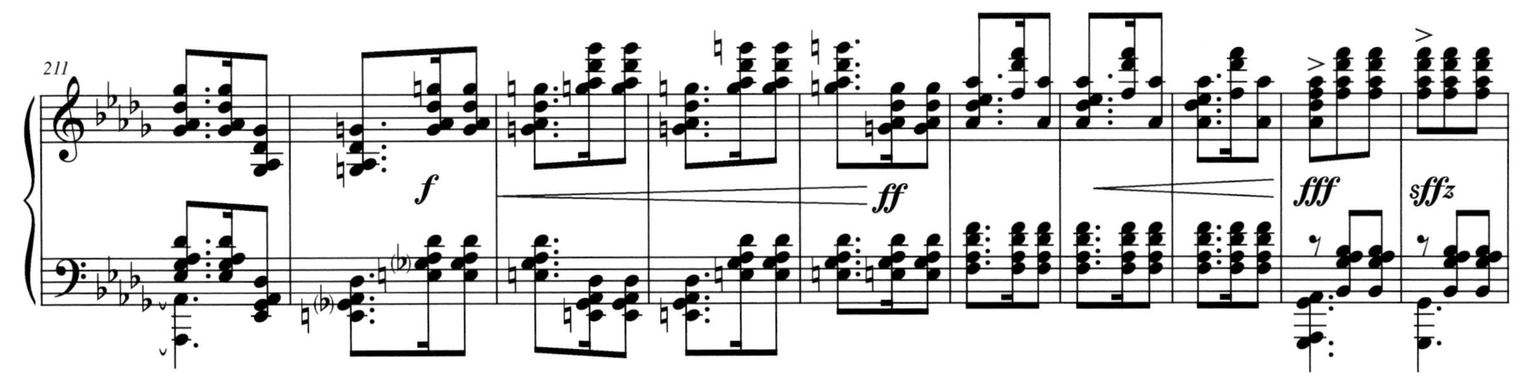
211
f
ff
fff
sffz

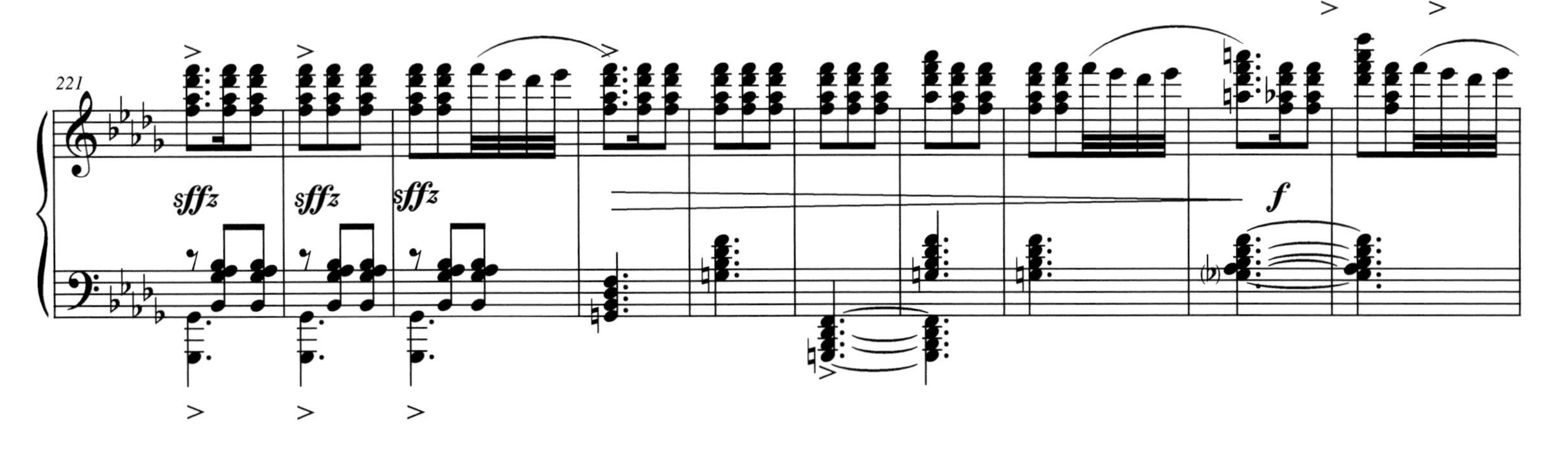
221
sffz
sffz
sffz
f

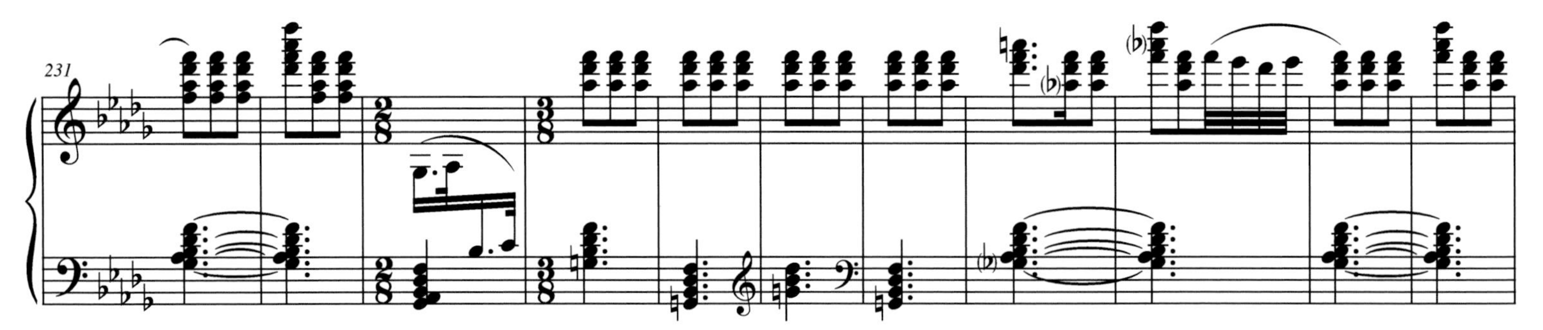

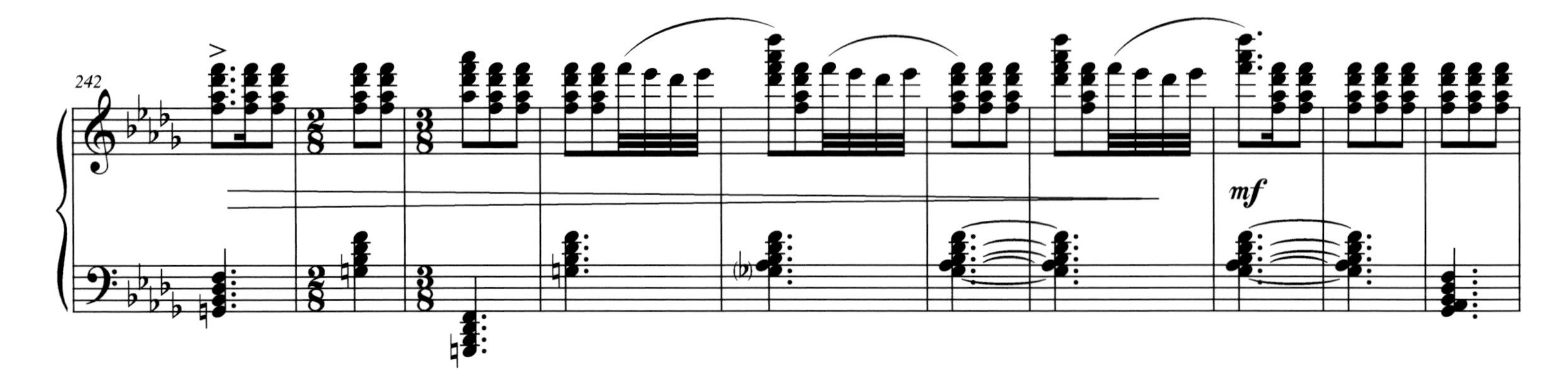

♩= 100

262

p

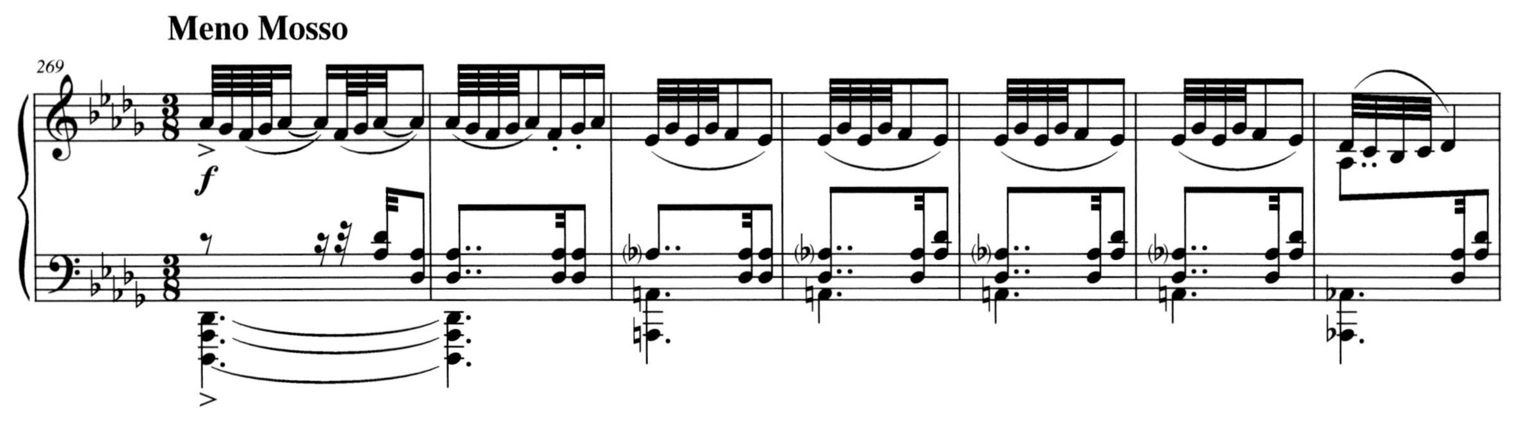

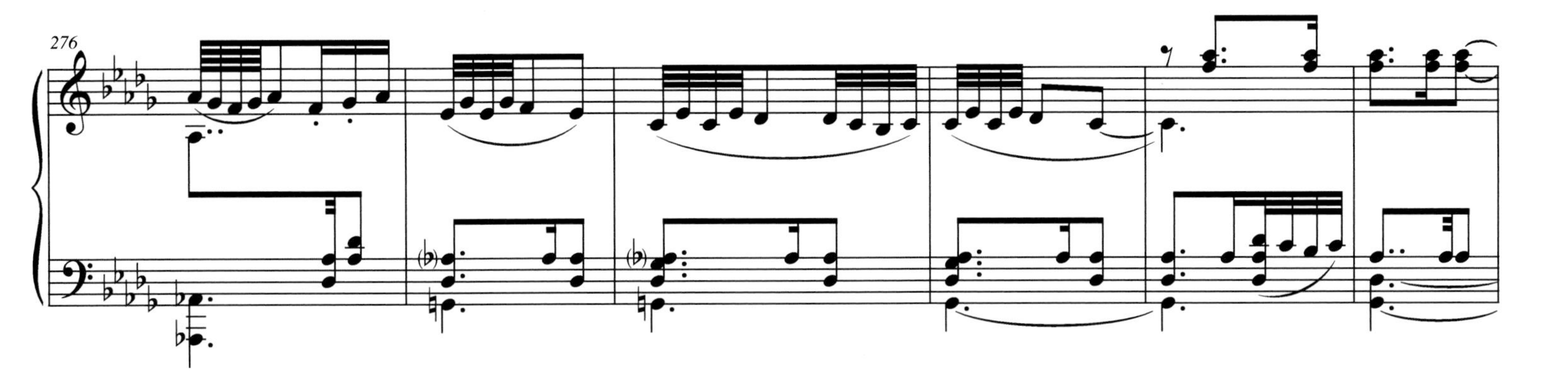
276

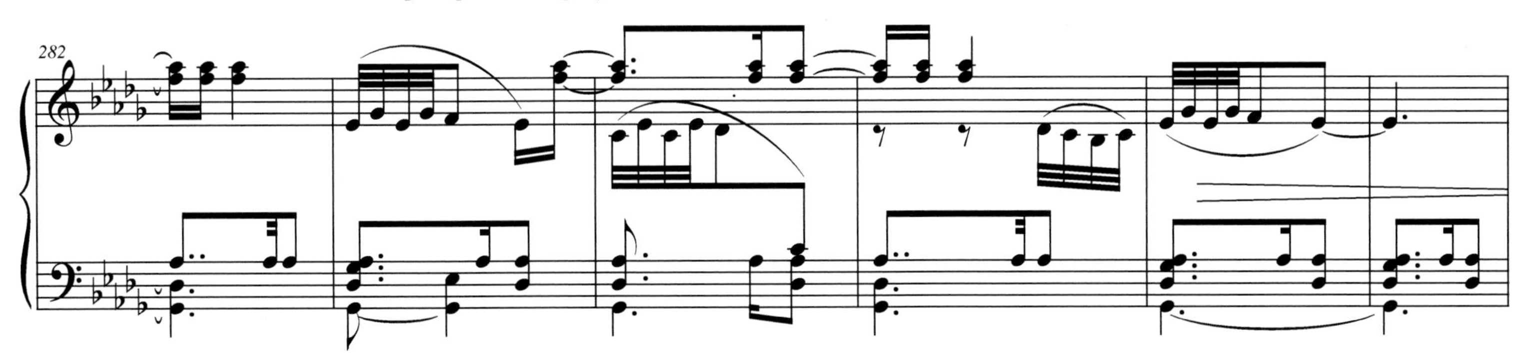
getting ever so slightly slower and slower
282

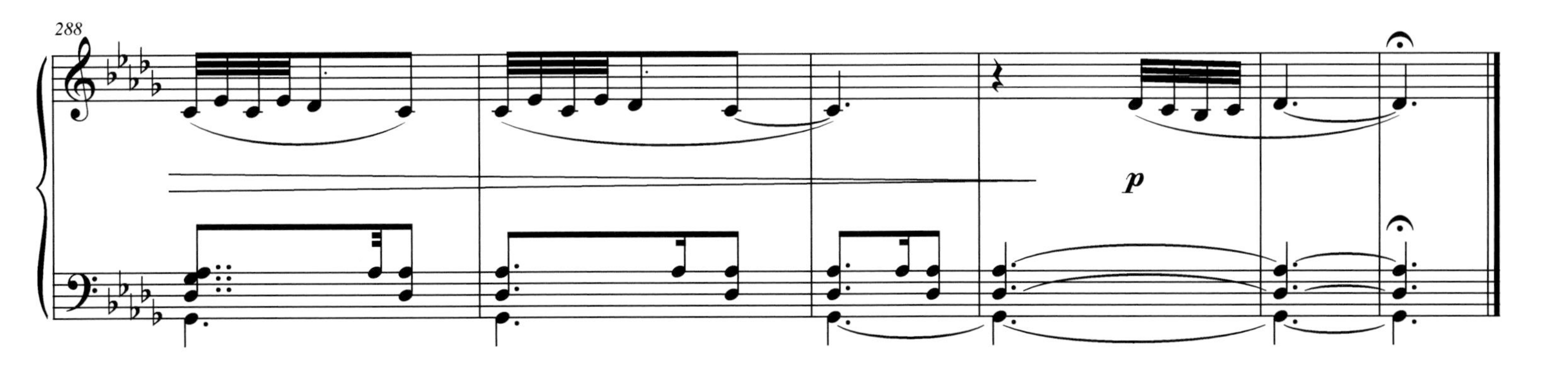
288
p